Michael
Rosen

Smacking My Lips

PENGUIN BOOKS

PENGUIN BOOKS

Published by the Penguin Group
Penguin Books Ltd, 27 Wrights Lane, London W8 5TZ, England
Penguin Books USA Inc., 375 Hudson Street, New York, New York 10014, USA
Penguin Books Australia Ltd, Ringwood, Victoria, Australia
Penguin Books Canada Ltd, 10 Alcorn Avenue, Toronto, Ontario, Canada M4V 3B2
Penguin Books (NZ) Ltd, 182–190 Wairau Road, Auckland 10, New Zealand

Penguin Books Ltd, Registered Offices: Harmondsworth, Middlesex, England

First published in *Quick, Let's Get Out of Here* by André Deutsch Ltd 1983
Published in Puffin Books 1985

This collection published in Penguin Books 1996
1 3 5 7 9 10 8 6 4 2

Copyright © Michael Rosen, 1983
All rights reserved

The moral right of the author has been asserted

Set in 12.5/13pt Bembo Monotype
Typeset by Datix International Limited, Bungay, Suffolk
Printed in England by Clays Ltd, St Ives plc

Contents

Quick, Let's Get Out of Here

Once I was round a friend's place
and just as we were going out
he went over to the table
and picked a hard lump of chewed-up
chewing gum with teeth marks in it
off the table top
and stuffed it in his mouth.

His gran was there and she said,
'You're not taking that filthy thing
with you, are you?'
And he said to me,
'Quick – let's get out of here.'

Tricks

Nearly every morning
my brother would lie in bed,
lift his hands up in the air
full stretch
then close his hands around an invisible bar.
'Ah, my magic bar,' he'd say.
Then he'd heave on the bar,
pull himself up,
until he was sitting up in bed.

Then he'd get up.
I said,
'You haven't got a magic bar above your bed.'
'I have,' he said.
'You haven't,' I said.
'Don't believe me then,' he said.
'I won't – don't worry,' I said.
'It doesn't make any difference to me
if you do or you don't,' he said,
and went out of the room.

'Magic bar!' I said.
'Mad. He hasn't got a magic bar.'
I made sure he'd gone downstairs,
then I walked over to his bed
and waved my hand about in the air
above his pillow.
'I knew it,' I said to myself.
'Didn't fool me for a moment.'

Washing Up

On Sundays,
my mum and dad said,
'Right, we've cooked the dinner,
you two can wash it up,'
and then they went off to the front room.

So then we began.
First there was the row about who
was to wash and who was to dry.
My brother said, 'You're too slow at washing,
I have to hang about waiting for you,'
so I said,
'You always wash, it's not fair.'

'Hard cheese,' he says,
'I'm doing it.'
So that was that.

'Whoever dries has to stack the dishes,'
he says,

so that's me stacking the dishes
while he's getting the water ready.

Now,
quite often we used to have mustard
with our Sunday dinner
and we didn't have it out of a tube,
one of us used to make it with the powder
in an eggcup
and there was nearly always
some left over.

Anyway,
my brother
he'd be washing up by now
and he's standing there at the sink
his hands in the water,
I'm drying up,
and suddenly he goes,
'Quick, quick quick
come over here
quick, you'll miss it
quick, you'll miss it.'

'What?' I say, 'What?'
'Quick, quick. In here,
in the water.'
I say,

'What? What?'
'Give us your hand,' he says
and he grabs my hand
then my finger,
'What?' I say,
'That,' he says,
and he pulls my finger under the water
and stuffs it into the eggcup
with left-over blobs of old mustard
stuck to the bottom.
It's all slimey.
'Oh Horrible.'

I was an idiot to have believed him.
So I go on drying up.

Suddenly
I feel a little speck of water on my neck.

I look up at the ceiling
Where'd that come from?

I look at my brother
he's grinning all over his big face

'Oy, cut that out,'
He grins again
sticks his finger under the water
in the bowl and
flicks.
Plip.
'Oy, that got me right on my face.'
'Did it? did it? did it?'
He's well pleased.

So now it's my turn
I've got the drying up cloth, haven't I?
And I've been practising for ages
on the kitchen door handle.
Now he's got his back to me
washing up
and

out goes the cloth, like a whip, it goes
right on the –
'Ow – that hurt. I didn't hurt *you*.'
Now it's me grinning.

So he goes,
'All right, let's call it quits.'
'OK,' I say, 'one-all. Fairy squarey.'

So I go on drying up.
What I don't know is that
he's got the Fairy Liquid bottle under the
      water
boop boop boop boop boop boop
it's filling up
with dirty soapy water
and next thing it's out of the water
and he's gone squeeeesh
and squirted it right in my face.

'Got you in the mush,' he goes.

'Right, that's it,' I say,
'I've had enough.'
And I go upstairs and get
this old bicycle cape I've got,
one of those capes you can wear
when you ride a bicycle in the rain.

So I come down in that
and I say,
'OK I'm ready for anything you've got now.
You can't get me now, can you?'

So next thing he's got the little
washing-up brush
and it's got little bits of meat fat
and squashed peas stuck in it
and he's come up to me
and he's in, up, under the cape with it
working it round and round
under my jumper, and under my chin.

So that makes me really wild
and I make a grab for anything that'll

hold water; dip it in the sink
and fling it at him.

What I don't know is that
while I went upstairs to get the cape
he's got a secret weapon ready.
It's his bicycle pump,
he's loaded it with the dirty washing-up water
by sucking it all in.
He picks it up,
and it's squirt again.
All over my hair

Suddenly the door opens.
'Have you finished the . . .?'
It's Mum AND Dad.

'Just look at this.
Look at the pair of them.'

And there's water all over the floor
all over the table
10   and all we've washed up is

two plates and the mustard pot.

My dad says,
'You can't be trusted to do anything you're asked,
can you.'

He always says that.

Mind you, the floor was pretty clean
after we had mopped it all up.

Mystery

CRASH!!!
DAD: What was that noise?
SON: The bowl. I've broken the bowl.
MUM: What bowl?
SON: The one with lines on.
DAD: How did you break it?
SON: I was balancing it on my head.
DAD: The boy's mad.
MUM: How else is he going to practise?
DAD: Why were you balancing it on your head?
SON: I was pretending it was a hat.
DAD: Why do you need to practise pretending a
    bowl is a hat?
SON: (NO ANSWER)

The Watch

My mum and dad gave me a watch.
Not a posh watch
Good enough to tell the time by, though.
And it went well enough
until one day at a camp
we were playing smugglers and customs
over the sand dunes.

I was a smuggler
and I had to get £20,000
through the customs
for us to win the game.
£20,000 written on a piece of paper.
There were three ways to get past
the customs.
One – by running so fast
the customs couldn't catch you.
Two – by going creepy-crawly so they couldn't see
    you.
Three – going through the customs

13

with it hidden somewhere.

I chose three.
I chose to hide it on me somewhere.
But where?
'I know,' I said,
'I'll stuff it in my watch,'
and I took the back off my watch
folded up the piece of paper
with £20,000 written on it
and clipped the back of my watch on.

So then I went creepy-crawly over the sand dunes.
They saw me
they grabbed me
and they searched me.
They looked in my pockets
they looked in my shoes
they looked in my socks
they looked up my jumper
down my jumper
down my shirt
14   in my armpits.

They even looked *under* my watch
but they never thought to look
in my watch, did they?

So they let me go –

and when I got to the other end
where the other smugglers were
I said,
'Hooray, I got through.'
I opened up the back of my watch
and there it was –
£20,000.
I took it out – handed it over
and we had won the game.
I snapped the back of my watch on –
looked at the time and –
my watch. It had stopped.
It was broken.
I had broken it.
That evening I told my brother all about it
and I said,
'Don't tell Mum or Dad about it

or I'll get into trouble.
I'll get it mended secretly.'

So there we were, tea-time
and my brother suddenly goes,
'What's the time, Mick?'
and I went all red and flustered
and I go,
'er er,'
and I look at my watch
and I go,
'er er about six o'clock.'
'No it's not,' says my dad.
'It's seven o'clock,'
and he sees me going red.
'Is your watch going wrong?'
'Er – no.'
'Let's have a look.'
'No, it's all right.'
'Let me have a look. It's stopped,
it's broken. How did it get broken?'
'I don't know.'
'What do you mean you don't know.'

My brother was laughing all over his big face
without making a sound.

So then I told my dad
all about the smugglers and customs

and hiding the money in my watch.
He was furious.
'We gave you the watch
so you could tell the time
not for you to use as part of a secret agent's
smuggling outfit.
Well, don't expect us to buy you
presents like that again.'

I was *so* angry with my brother
for getting me into trouble.
Inside I was bubbling.
So –
as soon as tea was over
I went down to our backyard
where there was an old cherry tree
and I broke a twig off it.

It was all prickly and flakey
and covered in a kind of grey slimy muck.

So then I took this twig back upstairs
into our bedroom
and I'll tell you what I did with it.
I shoved it into his bed.
And as I shoved it into his bed
I thought
'This'll pay him back.
This'll pay him back.
This'll pay him back.

He's going to get into bed tonight
after I'm asleep
and his feet
are going to get all
prickled up
and covered in grey mucky slimy stuff.'

Well, later that evening
I was doing some homework
and I had some really hard sums to do.

I couldn't do them.
I was stuck
and my brother – he sees me
scribbling out all these numbers
and the page is a mess
so my brother, he says,
'What's up? Do you want a bit of help
with your sums?'
What could I say to that?
At first, I go,
'No no, it's all right.'
But he goes,
'No, come on – I'll lend you a hand.'
So I say, 'OK'
and he comes over and he helped me.
He's sitting there right next to me,
my enemy,
showing me how to do my sums.
Then he said,
'Now you try,'
and then *I* could do them.

So there I was, friends with him,
grateful,
I'm saying, 'Thanks. Thanks for helping me.'
But in the back of my mind,
I know something
THE TWIG WAS STILL IN THE BED.

I didn't know what to say.
All I could see was
THE TWIG
sitting in his bed
just where his feet would get it.

Even if I went and got it out

there'd still be a heap of dirty prickly bits
left in his bed,
after he's showed me how to get all the sums right.

So I go,
'Look – when you go to bed –
tonight
20 there'll be a twig in your bed.'

So he goes,
'A twig in my bed? A twig in my bed?
How did it get there then?'

So I say,
'I put it there.'
And my mum and dad heard that.
So my dad goes,
'You put a twig in his bed?
Did I hear that right?
You put a twig in his bed, might I ask
Why did you put a twig in his bed?'
And I just couldn't say.
I just sat there like a lemon.
I couldn't say it was to pay him back for
telling on me about the watch
because they wouldn't think there was anything
   wrong
with him doing that.
So I just sat there
and then I said,
'I don't know.'
What a stupid thing to say.

My dad goes,
'You don't know why you put a twig in his bed?
You don't know why?
The boy's going mad.
First thing he does is smash up his watch
and next thing
he's going round stuffing a twig in people's beds.
He's going stark staring mad, I tell you.'

I didn't think I was going mad.
And I don't think my brother did.

I bet *he* knew why I put
a twig in his bed . . .

Eddie and the Gerbils

Not long ago
we went on holiday with some people
who've got gerbils.
We haven't got any pets
and Eddie (he was two years old)
he thought they were
WONDERFUL.
He was always looking in their cage
going,
'Hallo gerbils, hallo gerbils, hallo gerbils.'
And when the boys took them out of the cage
Eddie loved stroking them,
going,
'Hallo gerbils, hallo gerbils, hallo gerbils,'
all over again.

Now,
when we got home from the holiday
Like I said,
we haven't got any pets.

What we've got, is
MICE.
So we wanted to get rid of them.
So we rang up the council to ask for the mouse-man
to come over and get rid of them.
The mouse-man.
That's not a man who is a mouse.
Silly,
it's a man who comes over
and he goes round
sniffing along the walls
and behind cupboards
to find where the mice go.
Then he puts down these little trays of poison,
only the mice don't know it's poison,
they think it's some really nice stuff
like biscuits.
And this poison
it burns them up from the inside
And they just die.
The dead ones pong a bit.
The bloke puts down little trays of this poison
24 and the mice find it and go,

'Wow. This looks really tasty stuff,'
gobble gobble gobble
clunk. Dead.
gobble gobble gobble
clunk.

So one morning we're having breakfast
and when Eddie has breakfast
sometimes he sits at the table
sometimes he sits on the table
sometimes he sits under the table.
Well,
this particular morning
he was sitting under the table.
So I'm eating my breakfast
munch munch munch
and suddenly I hear
'Hallo gerbils.'
'Uh?' Ignore it. Munch munch munch.
'Hallo gerbils.'
Better have a look.
Oh no.
He's got a dead mouse in his hand.

Clutching it.
Head poking out the top of his fist
tail out the bottom.
And he's stroking it.
The dead mouse.
And he's going,
'Hallo gerbils hallo gerbils hallo gerbils.'
I go,
'No Eddie, No Eddie. It's not a gerbil.
It's a mouse. A dead mouse.'
And he shakes his head and he goes,
'Na na. Gerbils.'
'No, Eddie. Give it here.'
So I took hold of it.
By the tail.
And I took it over to the bin
and he's following behind me on his little legs
and I dropped it in the bin
and he comes over to the bin too
and he looks up, all sad.
And he goes,
'Oh.
Bye bye gerbils.'

Wise One

Wise one, wise one
how long is a piece of string?

Twice as long as half its length.

Wise one, wise one
how do you kill a snake?

Put its tail in its mouth
and it'll eat itself up.

Wise one, wise one
What's at the end of a cat's tail?

A cat.

Wise one, wise one
How can I get a chick out of a boiled egg?

Feed it to the chicken
so it can lay it again.

Wise one, wise one
Why do bricklayers put mortar on bricks?

To keep the bricks together
and to keep the bricks apart.

Wise one, wise one
My parrot talks too much.

Give it a good book to read.

End of the World

Sometimes it looks as if it could be
the end of the world:

earthquakes
volcanoes
hurricanes
floods

sometimes it's lightning at night
and there's thunder in your ears.

It could be
the end of the world.

Sometimes you hear
small boys and girls
howling,
'I've dropped my lolleeeeeeeeeee,'
or
'He's got my sweeteeeeeeeeeeeeees,'

and Mum or Dad say to them:
'It's not the end of the world you know.'

They think it is.

Money Box

My first money box
was a yellow house
with a green roof.
On the roof
was a yellow woodpecker.
On the woodpecker there was
a green beak.
In his beak was
a slot.
In the slot,
went your money.
At that –
the yellow woodpecker pecked the chimney
on the green roof
of the yellow house
and the money rolled down the beak,
down the chimney
and into the house.
Eeeeeeeeeewwwwwwwww clunk.
Funny thing is:

31

I can't remember how I got the money out!

My next money box
was A Money Box.
A wooden box with a trick drawer.
You opened the drawer
you put the money in the drawer
you closed the drawer
and when you pulled the drawer out –
it was empty – the money was gone.

My friends came over.

'OK,' I said,
'you put your money in the drawer,
close the drawer,
pull the drawer out
and your money's gone.
It's in the box.'

'How does it work?'

32   'Not saying.'

'Well, I'm not putting my money in it then.'

'Well, you won't see it work then, will you?'

'All right – one penny – there.'

'In goes the drawer, out it comes – see – the penny's
   gone.'

'How do I get it back then?'

'Secret.'

Newcomers

My father came to England
from another country
My father's mother came to England
from another country
but my father's father
stayed behind.

So my dad had no dad here
and I never saw him at all.

One day in spring
some things arrived:
a few old papers,
a few old photos
and – oh yes –
a hulky bulky thick checked jacket
that belonged to the man
I would have called 'Grandad'.
The Man Who Stayed Behind.

But I kept that jacket
and I wore it
and I wore it
and I wore it
till it wore right through
at the back.

Christmas Stocking

They say:
Leave a stocking out for Santa.
And somehow or another
this friendly old bloke's going
to get round every one of us
in one night
and fill it up.

Me and my brother –
we had a plan.
Not just one stocking
Not just two stockings
no – we emptied the chest of drawers
of every sock we could find
and laid them out on the end of the bed,
hanging from the window,
the door handle,
the lamp shade
and the mantelpiece –
we covered the place with socks.

Then we went to sleep.

I don't know what the old bloke thought when he
  came
but he must have turned up and said:
'Well – that little show doesn't fool me,'
and he stuffed a few sweets in one sock
just one single solitary sock,
and left.

At least,
that's what Mum and Dad
thought he did.

Chocolate Cake

I love chocolate cake.
And when I was a boy
I loved it even more.

Sometimes we used to have it for tea
and Mum used to say,
'If there's any left over
you can have it to take to school
tomorrow to have at playtime.'
And the next day I would take it to school
wrapped up in tin foil
open it up at playtime and sit in the
corner of the playground
eating it,
you know how the icing on top
is all shiny and it cracks as you
bite into it
and there's that other kind of icing in
the middle
and it sticks to your hands and you

can lick your fingers
and lick your lips
oh it's lovely.
yeah.

Anyway,
once we had this chocolate cake for tea
and later I went to bed
but while I was in bed
I found myself waking up
licking my lips
and smiling.
I woke up proper.
'The chocolate cake.'
It was the first thing
I thought of.
I could almost see it
so I thought,
what if I go downstairs
and have a little nibble, yeah?
It was all dark
everyone was in bed
so it must have been really late

but I got out of bed,
crept out of the door

there's always a creaky floorboard, isn't there?

Past Mum and Dad's room,

careful not to tread on bits of broken toys
or bits of Lego
you know what it's like treading on Lego
with your bare feet,

yowwww
shhhhhhh

downstairs
into the kitchen
open the cupboard
and there it is
all shining.

So I take it out of the cupboard
put it on the table

and I see that
there's a few crumbs lying about on the plate,
so I lick my finger and run my finger all over the
    crumbs
scooping them up
and put them into my mouth.

ooooooooommmmmmmmm

nice.

Then
I look again
and on one side where it's been cut,
it's all crumbly.
So I take a knife
I think I'll just tidy that up a bit,
cut off the crumbly bits
scoop them all up
and into the mouth

oooooommm   mmmm
nice.

Look at the cake again.

That looks a bit funny now,
one side doesn't match the other
I'll just even it up a bit, eh?

Take the knife
and slice.
This time the knife makes a little cracky noise
as it goes through that hard icing on top.

A whole slice this time,

into the mouth.

Oh the icing on top
and the icing in the middle
ohhhhhh oooo mmmmm.

But now
I can't stop myself.
Knife —
I just take any old slice at it

and I've got this great big chunk
and I'm cramming it in
what a greedy pig
but it's so nice,

and there's another
and another and I'm squealing and I'm smacking my lips
and I'm stuffing myself with it
and
before I know
I've eaten the lot.
The whole lot.
I look at the plate.
It's all gone.

Oh no
they're bound to notice, aren't they,
a whole chocolate cake doesn't just disappear
does it?

What shall I do?

I know. I'll wash the plate up,

and the knife
and put them away and maybe no one
will notice, eh?

So I do that
and creep creep creep
back to bed
into bed
doze off
licking my lips
with a lovely feeling in my belly.
Mmmmmmmmmm.

In the morning I get up,
downstairs,
have breakfast,
Mum's saying,
'Have you got your dinner money?'
and I say,
'Yes.'
'And don't forget to take some chocolate cake with
    you.'
44 I stopped breathing.

'What's the matter,' she says,
'you normally jump at chocolate cake?'

I'm still not breathing,
and she's looking at me very closely now.
She's looking at me just below my mouth.
'What's that?' she says.
'What's what?' I say.
'What's that there?'
'Where?'
'There,' she says, pointing at my chin.
'I don't know,' I say.
'It looks like chocolate,' she says.
'It's not chocolate cake is it?'
No answer.
'Is it?'
'I don't know.'
She goes to the cupboard
looks in, up, top, middle, bottom,
turns back to me.
'It's gone.
It's gone.
You haven't eaten it, have you?'

'I don't know.'
'You don't know? You don't know if you've eaten a
  whole chocolate cake or not?
When? When did you eat it?'

So I told her,

and she said
well what could she say?
'That's the last time I give you any chocolate cake to
  take to school.
Now go. Get out
no wait
not before you've washed your dirty sticky face.'
I went upstairs
looked in the mirror
and there it was,
just below my mouth,
a chocolate smudge.
The give-away.
Maybe she'll forget it by next week.

Losing Things

I HATE LOSING THINGS
so I think,
'What if
there is a place somewhere
where everything you ever lost
goes?'

Somehow or another
all those things you ever lost
found their way there –
to this place?

Maybe there's a huge hall somewhere
with hundreds and hundreds of doors
and one of the doors
has got your name on it.

I see myself
going to this huge hall one day.

The way in is not very big
but once you get inside –
it's enormous.
It's cold and dark and damp
and there are thousands of people there,
and they're all looking for the door
that belongs to them
the door with their name on it.
Everyone is asking everyone else:
'Have you seen my door?'
'What's your name?'
And people are saying things like –
'I think I saw it over there.'
or
'Don't bother me, I'm looking for mine.'

So I begin to look
and I walk about
and I ask someone:
'Have you seen my door?'
'I think it's over there,' she says.
So I go over there –
but it isn't.

So I go on wandering around the big hall.
I ask someone: 'Have you seen my door?'
and someone says,
'Up the spiral stair –
it's on the second floor.'
On the way there
someone stops me and says,
'Have you seen my door?'
and I say, 'No, I haven't.'
I climb up the spiral stair
on to the second floor
but my door isn't there either.

So I go on wandering around the big hall

And someone comes up to me and says,
'Have you seen my door?'
'Have you seen mine?' I say.
'It's at the end by the steel doors,'
and it is.

It's my door
It's got my name on it.

I knock on the door
'Who's there?'
'Me.'
'We were expecting you.'
The bolts draw back,
the door opens
and two old people let me in
and shut the door behind me.

'It's all here,' one of them says.
'It's all here,' the other one says.

And they're right.

There's my penknife from Switzerland,
I lost when I was twelve
the old watch I lost in my car accident
my blue anorak with the hood
that I left on a railway station in Paris
my round gold sun-glasses
that I once wore in a play
to make me look blind
the football

that was a birthday present
that I lost on the same day I got it
over a wall in the burnt out church.
They're all there.

A black white and green towel,
a moroccan leather wallet.

'They're all here,' says one of the old people.
'They're all here,' says the other.

'Have you got a bag to take them away in?'
says one.
'Here's a bag to take them away in,' says the other.
So I fill up the bag
with all the things that I've ever lost
until all the shelves are empty.

'Come back and see us anytime,' says one.
'Come back and see us,' says the other.
'You know where we are now, don't you?' says one.
'You know where we are,' says the other.

'But you're taking my name off the door,' I say.
'Why are you taking my name off the door?'
'Because you know where we are now, don't you?'
    says one.
'You know where we are,' says the other.
And they shut the door.
I hear the locks and bolts on the door

and I walk away into the crowd
in the huge hall,
and everyone is still walking round
asking everyone else,
'Do you know where my door is?'

A tall man with a steering wheel in his hand
says to me,
'You seen my door, have you?'
'No,' I say. 'No.'
'No, I don't expect you have,' he says.

I look round to see if I can remember
where my door was.
52   And it's out of sight.

Too many people are in the way.
So I say to myself,
'One day,
I'll try and find my way back there,'
but something tells me,
some little voice in my head says,
'I bet you'll never ever find that door again.
You've had the only chance
you'll ever have.'

So I make my way
out of that huge dark hall
with the thousands and thousands of doors
and the thousands and thousands of people

and I hurry home with my bag
and I get back to my room
and I spread out on the floor
all those things that I had lost
and I've now got back again,

and that makes me very happy.

I'm Not Going Places With Them Again

When we went to Chessington Zoo
with the club
we all went in
and the leader said,
'Right, listen, everyone
listen, everyone,
everyone listen.
You can all go off where you like
for the next two hours
and we'll all meet up here
at 4 o'clock.
At 4 o'clock,
OK?'

Then we all went off
where we liked.
I saw the lions
and the seals
and the parrots

and the giraffes
and the crocodiles.
I ate my cheese and pickle sandwiches
a packet of crisps
and drank some of my fizzy orange
and ate a chocolate swiss roll.

Then I asked someone the time
and she said, '4 o'clock,'
so I went back to where we had to meet.

When I got there
everyone started shouting at me.

'Where have you been?
Where do you think you've been?
We've been looking for you for hours
we couldn't find you anywhere
we've scarcely had a chance to see
any of the animals
where have you been?'
I looked at them
and I said,

'I've been walking round the zoo.
I'm on time, aren't I?'
So then they started shouting at me again.

'You weren't supposed
to wander off on your own, were you?
You were supposed to be in your
group.
Everyone else was in their
groups.
You weren't, were you?'

'No.'

'Well, we've got to go now.
Just think, you've spoiled
everyone's afternoon, now.'

I listened to all that
but I wasn't sorry.
They said,
'You can all go off now.'
They didn't say anything about

groups.

What groups?

I'm not going places with them again.